Contents

1

About me

Come along and take a look,
There's lots about me in this book.
Read the boxes if you're eager
To see what happens when you're a Beaver.

This book belongs to...

I became a Beaver Scout
and made my Promise on...

I like Beaver Scouts because...

Draw around your hand

When you join the Cub Scouts you will be able to see how much you have grown.

My Colony

We live in our Lodges with sisters and brothers,
Like you in your Colony with lots of others.
Here you can show that you belong,
By filling in as you go along.

My Colony's name is...

_____

My Leaders' names and phone numbers are...

_____

_____

_____

_____

Did you know?
Beavers eat bark and roots that they find around the riverbank.

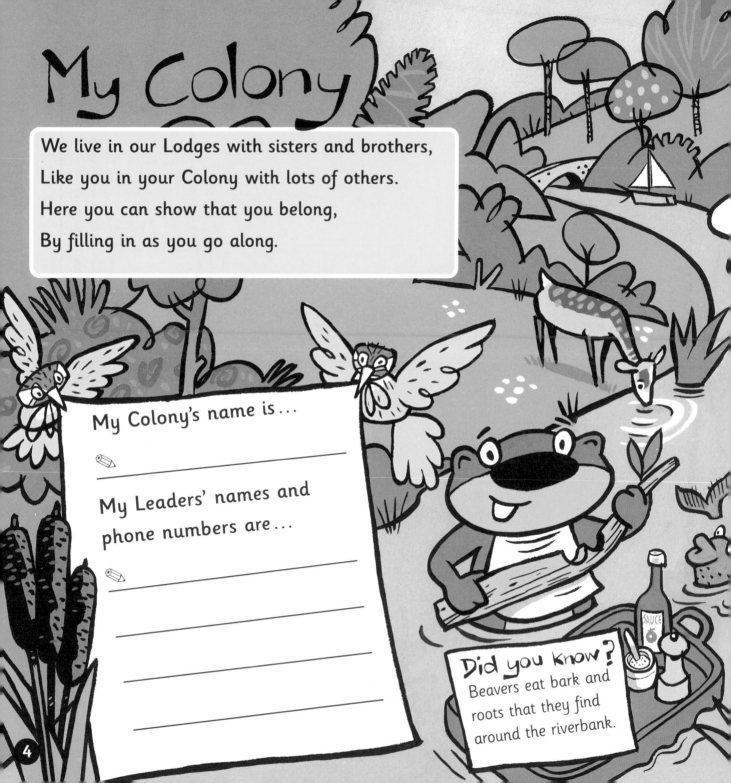

This is when my
Colony meets.
Draw the time of your
meeting on the clock.

**In my Beaver Scout Colony,
my friends are...**

We meet on this day.
Tick the day you meet.

MONDAY
TUESDAY
WEDNESDAY
THURSDAY
FRIDAY
SATURDAY
SUNDAY

At Beaver Scouts I wear
a uniform like this.

Colour this scarf in your Group's
colours. Everyone else in your Scout
Group wears a scarf like this too.

Becoming a Beaver Scout

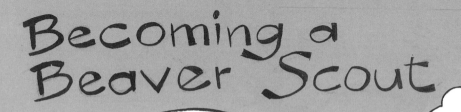

So now you want to join our crew,
It's hard at first when you are new.
But don't you worry, you'll find out,
Just what Scouting's all about.

Did you know?
Beavers have orange front teeth!

The Beaver Scout Promise

I promise to do my best, to be kind and helpful and to love God.

Try to learn the Promise for your Investiture.

Your Investiture is a special day when you make your Promise for the first time. Then you become a member of your Colony and the worldwide Scout Movement. Your Leader will tell you more about what will happen at your Investiture.

Scout Sign
This is a special sign that all Scouts make when they say their Promise.

scouts
be prepared . . .

Be prepared
This is the motto of all Members of the Scout Movement.

Handshake
Beaver Scouts shake with their left hand as a sign of friendship.

Badges
These are the badges you will get at your investiture:

COUNTY or AREA
DISTRICT
WORLD
NAME TAPE

Can you find the badges in the wordsearch on the sweatshirt?

```
B C O U N T Y I Q D U P
E G R O A N T R Y I M K
Z O I D M W V N A S B C
L H A R E A U H S T X P
I G F B T W E W G R E H
V I N E A Y O U E I J L
I F D G P W E R D C E O
Z B A T E H O N L T Y K
L L M V K O P R U D Q S
```

7

The family of Scouts

As a Beaver Scout you are a member of the Scout family.

You are all Scouts!

Beaver Scouts
age 6 – 8

Cub Scouts
age 8 – 10½

Scouts
age 10½ – 14

Explorer Scouts
age 14 – 18

the Scout Network
age 18 – 25

A short history of the Scouts

Scouting was the idea of Lor
Robert Baden-Powell.

Scouting began in 1907.

Beaver Scouts officially starte
in the United Kingdom in 19

Scouting around the world

There are over 28 million Scouts in the world today.

Did you know?

A beaver can close its nose and ears to block out water.

When is a Beaver Scout not a Beaver Scout?

Beaver Scouts have a different name in some countries of the world. In Australia they are called Joey Scouts.

How many fish can you see?

_____

What sort of things do Beaver Scouts do?

Chatting with friends

Playing games

Meeting new people

Having quiet moments

Going outdoors

What's your favourite? What's the best?
Time to get it off your chest.
Take a look at what we do,
You could soon be doing it too.

Badges

Talk to your Leader if you want to try for any of the badges on this page.

When you have been a Beaver Scout for one year, you will get a **Joining In Badge**.

Creative

Animal Friend

Experiment

There are five **Activity Badges** which are only for Beaver Scouts.

Discovery

Friendship

Outdoor

Explorer

You may get the chance to do **Challenge Badges**.

These badges show that you are trying new things.

Faith

Musician

IT

Nights Away

Swimming

There are four **Staged Activity Badges** which any Scout can try for at any time.

The Chief Scout's Bronze Award

Now you've really reached the top,
Just make sure that you don't stop.
What have you done? Make a list.
Are there things you might have missed?

When you are nearly old enough to leave the Beaver Scouts you can earn a special badge.

This is called the **Chief Scout's Bronze Award**.

To get this award you have to show that you have tried lots of new things. You can do this by earning some Challenge Badges.

Then you need to show that you have got better at something that you enjoy doing.

Did you know?

Beavers live in rivers and are good at swimming.

Beavers have tails that help them steer through water.

Beavers have four feet with five toes on each. Their back feet are webbed.

Here is a picture of me doing something I really enjoy.

What have I done as a Beaver Scout?

I expect by now you've had some fun.
Can you list the things you've done?
There are badges, outings, games and friends,
Beaver fun just never ends!

When you have been a Beaver Scout for a while, you will have done lots of things!

Use this page to make a note of the things you have done. It will help you remember them.

I got my first Joining In Badge on…
_____

I got my second Joining In Badge on…
_____

14

These are some of the outings I have been on...

These are some of the other special things I have done with my Colony...

Draw pictures of the Challenge Badges and Activity Badges you have earned.

Write the name of the badge next to your picture.

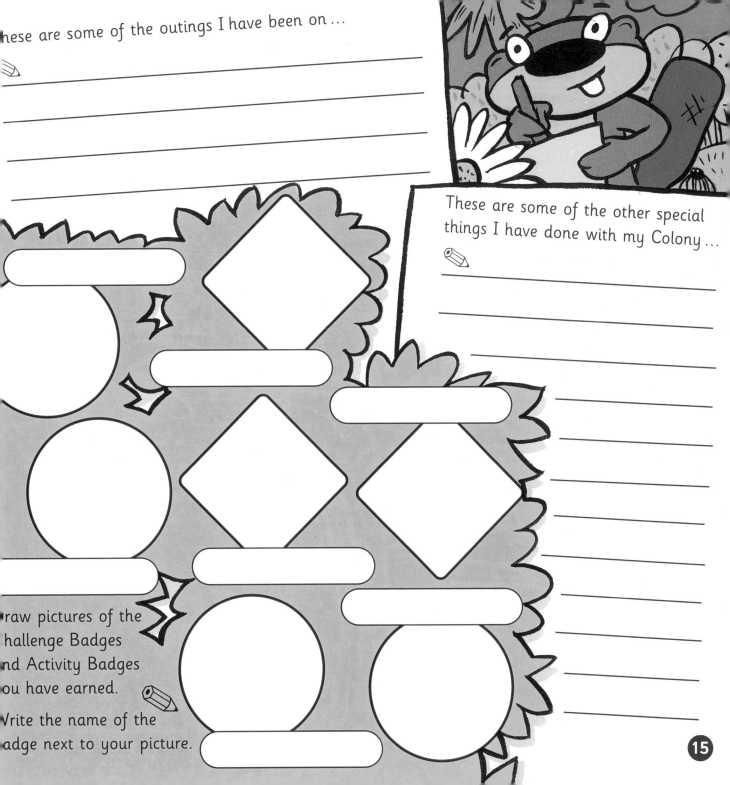

Moving on from Beaver Scouts

It's nearly time to say goodbye,
There are more things for you to try.
The next step up is the Cub Scout Pack,
So let's get going – don't look back!

By now you may have been a Beaver Scout for a long time. All the pages in this book will have filled up with the exciting things you have done.

Now it is time to think of some even more exciting things to do. Guess what?

You'll have just as much fun in the Cub Scout Pack!